NoBODY
LOOKS LIKE ME

ISBN: 978-1-7369900-3-2 (Paperback)
ISBN: 978-1-7369900-2-5 (Hardcover)

Library of Congress Control Number: 2021911038

Any references to historical events, real people, or real places are used fictitiously. Names, characters, and places are products of the author's imagination.

Printed by Ingram Spark, in the United States of America.

First printing edition 2021.

Publisher: My Adoptee Truth

This is Sarah.
Sarah was adopted.

Sarah doesn't look like anyone in her family.
Sarah has blonde hair, blue eyes, and a widow's peak.
Her family all have black hair and green eyes.
Sarah does not have their same eyes, nose, lips or hands.

Sarah looks in the mirror and wonders where her features come from, especially her bright blue eyes.

Because she does not see herself reflected in her adoptive mother's eyes, it is hard for Sarah to make and keep eye contact with her. The wrong eyes are always staring back.

Sarah searches the faces
of strangers walking down
the street,

wondering if
she's related
to any of them.

She daydreams about finding the perfect shade of blue eyes that match hers.

Sarah loves to be active. She is always playing outside,
riding her bike, or playing sports. Sarah's adoptive parents
do not enjoy being active.

It is confusing to grow up with people who do not look or act like you. She questions her body and does not build strong self-confidence because her personality and looks are not reflected by her adoptive family. Sarah does not know where she fits in the world.

When Sarah grows up she decides to have her own children.
When they are born she is in awe. They have blonde hair
and the same color of blue eyes. For the first time, Sarah
feels like she has found home.

- 16 -

Sarah later decides to search for her biological family. She and her children need to see other people who look and behave like them to feel grounded, like they have a genetic place in the world.

She meets her biological mother first. They resemble each other and Sarah is healed by knowing her story and that she was wanted.

Next Sarah finds her biological father. She does not see a picture of him so she cannot tell if they look alike.

Sarah calls him on the phone after sending him
a letter and photos of herself and family.

Unfortunately her biological
father is not interested in
knowing her. He says Sarah
is just bringing up the past.

Sarah does not give up. She knows she has two siblings from her biological father. Sarah wants to try all avenues to find all her biological relatives.

She is able to find her siblings through DNA testing and the help of a search angel.

When Sarah and her children see pictures of her
biological brother and sister, they get goose bumps.
They look exactly like her. Their noses are similar,
and their faces crease the same way when they smile.
Sarah's daughter has the same nose as her aunt.
Their eyes are all the same shade of blue.

And for the second time, Sarah feels at home.
A sense of trust and safety washes over her. There is
warmth in her heart and her body relaxes. She knows
instinctively that everything will work out the way it is
supposed to.

Sarah cannot stop staring at their pictures.
She loves them already.

When Sarah meets her siblings in person, they find out they have more in common than just eye color. They like skiing, hiking and traveling.

Sarah thinks about how much more confident she would have been seeing her own behaviors, personality and eyes reflected back to her from her brother and sister.

She sees that confidence now in her own children as they grow, they are free to be their own selves without questions.

By having her own children and reuniting with biological relatives, Sarah healed her lack of mirroring. They were the final missing pieces to heal her soul.

As Sarah parents her children, giving them what she wished she'd had, she can internally reparent herself.

Sarah must validate herself and step into her own power. By healing, Sarah reconnects with her body and reunites with her spirit, allowing her authentic self to finally be fully seen and appreciated.

"Thank you Anne, Lesli and Jon for your encouragement and support on this project. Thank you, Laura, for your perfect drawings. And thank you to all my biological family for being my mirrors."

9 781736 990025